Bee Tree

Piglet's House

Christopher Robin's House

Pooh's House

Tigger

Rabbit's House

First published in the UK in 2024 by Studio Press,
an imprint of Bonnier Books UK,
4th Floor, Victoria House, Bloomsbury Square, London WC1B 4DA
Owned by Bonnier Books, Sveavägen 56, Stockholm, Sweden

www.bonnierbooks.co.uk

1 3 5 7 9 10 8 6 4 2

ISBN 978-1-80078-762-9

Written by Catherine Hapka
Illustrated by Mike Wall
Edited by Stephanie Milton
Designed by Alessandro Susin
Production by Giulia Caparrelli

A CIP catalogue record for this book is available from the British Library

Printed and bound in China

For Linus and Verity

-Aunt Cathy

For Connor, this one's for you.

-Mike

THE *little* THINGS IN LIFE

Simple Reflections from the Hundred-Acre Wood

"Hello, new day.

It's lovely to meet you!"

Every new morning is a gift.

"Up, down, touch the ground . . .
I wonder what's for breakfast?"

looking forward to something pleasant
can be pleasant in itself.

"Oh, dear! Where, oh where, might a
hungry bear find a smackerel of honey?"

Why sit at home with an empty
belly when a friend might
have food to share?

"Christopher Robin, might
you have any honey to spare?"

*Being able to ask for help
is a strength, not a weakness.*

"Now, where could my lucky stone have gone?"

A thing need not be valuable
to be precious.

"Don't worry, Christopher Robin."

"We'll find it!"

It's best not to wait . . . .

to be asked
for help.

Offer it freely . . .

and from
the heart.

"It's all right, Pooh Bear. My lucky stone
will turn up. Things generally do."

Strive to understand what is meant,
not only what is said.

"How can a bear of very little brain find a
small but very important lucky stone?"

It's natural to doubt yourself from time to time, but if you keep questioning yourself you will find a way forwards.

"Think, think, think . . ."

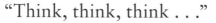

No moment spent in thought is wasted, no matter how long or short the moment or how large or small the thought.

"Where there are bees . . ."

Take time to notice the world around you . . .

". . . there is honey!"

. . . for a chance observation can lead to great things.

"But the honey wouldn't exist without the bees' hard work."

There's nothing like spending a day in nature to remind us that the world is full of miracles.

"To help Christopher Robin, I need more bees— er, I mean, friends."

Your friends are one of your greatest resources, and you are one of theirs.

"Perhaps a very small friend can help
find a very small lucky stone . . ."

"Of course I'll help, Pooh! Sweeping up
can wait."

There will always be lots to do - it's up to
you to decide what deserves your attention
most in any given moment.

"Is this a quest, Pooh?

It feels quite like a quest."

"I suppose it must

be one, then!"

Each new moment is an opportunity
for a new adventure.

"Oh, d-d-dear, dear. How will we ever
find one special stone among so many?"

"I don't know, Piglet. But we have to try."

When the task seems
overwhelming, focus on the
next small step and just keep
going, one step at a time.

"Hoo-hoo-hoo-HOO!
Some bouncin', huh?"

*Life is more fun when you
throw yourself at it wholeheartedly.*

"Will you help us with our quest, Tigger?"

"Sure thing, Buddy Bear!
  Questing's what tiggers do best!"

Confidence is contagious!

"Christopher Robin lost
somethin', huh?"

"Is it this?"

"Or this?"

"Gotta be this!"

"If anything is worth doing, do it with all your heart."
— Buddha

"Er, sorry, but I don't think any of these
are right, Tigger."

"It's okay, Piglet Ol' Pal. Findin'
'em was fun anyhoo-hoo-hoo-hoo!"

Failure is an opportunity to learn, and often
leads to future success.

"Oh, d-d-dear. Perhaps this quest
  is too difficult."

"Can we rest and then try again?"

Find a moment to recharge and
take care of your needs, and you're
more likely to succeed.

"Tiggers like questin' better than restin'!"

"Everyone has to rest sometime, Tigger."

"Well, almost everyone."

Take a mindful moment to notice what surrounds you.

"All this resting has made me
rather hungry."

"I've got an idea, Pooh Boy . . ."

Try not to let obstacles stand in the way of your dreams - they can often be overcome.

"Hallo, Rabbit! We're here!"

Paying a friend a visit is always a cause for celebration.

"I can see that, Tigger . . . especially as you
bounced all my radishes out of the barrow!"

Good friends can be honest with each other.

"We'll find your radishes, Rabbit!"

"Sure we will, Long Ears.
   We love quests!"

Everyone makes mistakes. Acknowledge
where you went wrong, but remember
to forgive yourself, too.

"Speaking of quests, Rabbit, will you join ours?"

"I'd like to help, Pooh.
  But my chores . . ."

Decisions, decisions . . .
Life is full of them.

"We'll help, Rabbit!"

Many hands make light work.

"Off we go!"

"Oh, d-d-dear. It's starting to rain!"

"That's great, little guy. Tiggers love rain!"

Try to appreciate the rain as well as the sun, the difficult as well as the simple.

"You're right, Tigger.
   Rain is fun!"

"Told ya, Pooh Boy.
   Fun is what tiggers do best!"

You're never too old to
play in puddles!

"Do you suppose the rain will
 ever stop, Pooh?"

"It has to sometime, Piglet."

Rain or shine, dark or light,
nothing stays the same forever.

"Tiggers do not like
   this much rain!"

"Oh, d-d-dear.
   I wish it would stop."

"I wish we were somewhere else . . ."

Some things in life are out of your control - it's best to focus on what you can change rather than what you can't.

"Somewhere . . ."

"Nicer."

"Warmer."

"Tastier."

"Toastier."

Even in dark times, you can
always discover the light.

"Come in, come in!

What are a few drips among friends?"

There is never a bad
time to be kind.

"Thanks, Owl.
  You made our wishes come true!"

"You saved the day, all right, Beak Lips.
  Marshmallow, anyone?"

"Thanks, Tigger.
  I'll have one, please."

"Can I pour you some tea?"

Few things in life are as gratifying
as a gathering of good friends.

"Is there anything cosier than listening
  to the sound of rain on the roof, Pooh?"

"Yes, Piglet. Doing the same thing
  with good friends."

Cherish every day . . .
every moment . . .
every drop of rain . . .
and every friend.

"Now that the rain has cleared, I am
fully prepared to lead the quest."

"Good thing I'm here, eh?"

Every leader needs willing followers.

"We're questing after something
small, you say? I spy something
small just there. Quest solved!"

"Er, Roo is a someone, not a
something, Owl."

Whenever you think you have all the answers, make sure you really listened to the questions.

"A quest?
  That sounds like fun!"

"Questing is very serious business,
  young Roo."

"Sure it is, Buddy Bird.
  But it's fun, too!"

A sprinkling of fun is like a pinch of salt
– it can make something good even better.

"Mama, may I go?
Please?"

Part of growing up is developing your sixth sense: a sense of adventure.

"Be careful, Roo!

And good luck with your quest, everyone!"

It costs nothing to wish someone well.

"Look, here's Eeyore!
  Maybe he can help!"

"Thanks for noticin' me, Roo.
  Hardly anyone does."

Seeing friends is always a happy occasion.
You never know what wonderful memories
might be created!

"You're questing for something small?
Pooh Sticks are small. And they end up
in unexpected places, too."

"Good point, Donkey Boy. We'd better
have a game, just in case!"

Play with the joy of a
child all your life, and you'll
never be old.

"It's getting dark!

Where will we sleep?"

"You can stay at my place if you like.
It's not much, but what it lacks in charm
it makes up for in dampness."

"The hand that gives, gathers."
-British proverb

"Thank you for sharing your house, Eeyore."

"You're welcome, Pooh. It may be a bit
cramped, but I will say I've
never been warmer."

Avoid hurting others' feelings
whenever possible - kindness costs nothing.

"Then again, it might be nearly as lovely
to sleep out under the stars."

*Be flexible and creative, and you
can overcome almost anything!*

"Look at that full moon!"

"Full of what, Owl?"

"Er, funny you should ask, Pooh.
I'll have to look that up once I'm back
with my books and learned papers."

Even the wise don't know everything.

"Oh, d-d-dear. Did you hear a sound, Pooh?"

"Yes. Take my hand, Piglet, and perhaps
  it will feel less scary for both of us."

When fears are shared, they can
seem less frightening.

"No sense questing on an empty stomach. What's for breakfast?"

"All I have is this thistle I was saving for myself. But I s'pose we could share."

"Er, thanks, Eeyore. But I have a better idea. Follow me."

The best things in life are not those you keep, but those you share.

"Hullo, everyone! You've been on a quest, you say? Please come in and tell me all about it over breakfast."

Allow yourself to be surprised especially by happiness, friendship, and kindness.

"What a magnificent adventure!
And what wonderful friends for trying
to find my lucky stone!"

A memory shines more brightly
when it's shared.

"But we didn't find it in the end."

"That's because my lucky stone wasn't
really lost, Pooh Bear. When I reached
into my pocket this morning, there
it was!"

Even when it's difficult, try your best
to be truthful with your friends.

"Looks like an ordinary stone to me.
What's so special about it?"

"Well, you see, Eeyore, I found this stone
on the very same day I first met Pooh
Bear. It reminds me how lucky I am to
have a friend like Pooh – and
all the rest of you, too!"

Even the simplest of objects can have
great value, not for themselves but for the
memories they hold.

"Hooray for lucky stones! And for quests!"

"Even though I had the thing you were
   questing for all along?"

There's no bad excuse for a party!

"True, we weren't sure exactly what we were doing or where we were going, and some difficult things happened. But we had some adventures, and we did it all together."

Allow yourself to be open to the journey, because the journey is the best part.

"But you spent an entire day on the quest!"

"And what more pleasant way to
spend a day than with friends,
trying to help another friend?"

Savour the little things in life, because someday you may realise they were the biggest things of all.

"Silly old bear!"

The End

N

Kanga and Roo's
Sandy Pit

Owls House

Rainy Area

Bridge

Eeyore's House